The Price Guide to

The Models of W.H. Goss

PRICE REVISION LIST

NOVEMBER 1982

INTRODUCTION

Little movement has occurred in the Goss market during 1982 and only around 10% of prices have moved, in nearly all cases upwards by some 10%-20%. Once again, models with matching arms have been very popular and almost without exception prices have increased strongly in this sector.

The reader is reminded that prices in *The Price Guide to the Models of W.H. Goss* and in this revision list are for models with any arms and that a premium must be added for any model which has the correct, or local, arms.

Cottages have again been the strongest single market and several major collections have appeared on the market during the year. These have been disposed of quickly and in many cases at new high prices. The sector has advanced by some 10% and shows little sign of slowing down.

It should be noted that any special crest or decoration adds a premium to the value of a model. For example, military, foreign, ecclesiastical, educational, commemorative, transfer printed, floral, flags of the Allies, verses, ancient armours and masonic decorations all add between £2 and £40 per piece, depending upon rarity.

All prices shown are for perfect pieces only. Whilst damaged items increase in value at the same rate as their perfect counterparts, a substantial allowance should be made for damage when buying or selling. Any chips, cracks, restoration, faded crests or rubbed gilding would reduce the value by some 50% to 90%. A large amount of material in rather dubious condition is now being found offered for sale by secondary dealers up and down the country. The only way to guard against being sold a damaged piece at a perfect price is to become an expert at checking china yourself or to obtain a receipt and money-back guarantee which any responsible dealer will gladly provide. It is perfectly acceptable to purchase a damaged piece — but only if the price fully allows for the imperfection.

Prices have remained strong this year, again largely due to the total lack of investors in the market and its dominance by genuine collectors. I forecast that world economies and the antique market would both continue to worsen and indeed they have. The collapse in the stamp, postcard and coin markets can only be fully appreciated when one tries to sell material in these fields. Heraldic china stands out as a strong, stable area and I have little doubt that it will continue to thrive during 1983 whilst the remainder of the antique market continues to decline. Once again, Goss collectors will sleep soundly during 1983.

Nicholas Pine

Goss

Page	Model No.	1981 £	1982 £
23	1a	5.00	5.00
	1b	7.50	7.50
	1c	22.50	27.50
	2	4.50	4.50
	3	16.00	16.00
	4	8.00	8.00
24	5	8.50	8.50
	6	7.50	7.50
	7	12.50	12.50
	8a	7.00	7.00
	8b	11.50	11.50
25	9	8.00	8.00
	10	28.00	30.00
	11	12.50	12.50
	12	25.00	25.00
26	13	16.50	16.50
	14	16.50	17.50
	15	85.00	85.00
	16a	4.00	4.00
	16b	12.00	12.00
27	17	19.50	22.50
	18	11.00	14.50
	19a	10.00	10.00
	19b	15.00	18.50
	20	9.00	9.00
28	21	7.00	7.00
	22	16.50	16.50
	23	7.00	7.50
	24	12.00	12.00
29	25	37.50	39.50
	26	13.50	15.50
	27	13.50	13.50
	28	8.00	10.00
30	29	7.00	7.50
	30a	6.50	6.50
	30b	10.00	10.00
	31	225.00	225.00
	32	16.00	16.00
31	33	7.00	7.00
	34	14.50	14.50
	35	5.00	5.00
	36a	7 00	7.00

Page	Model No.	1981 £	1982 £
	36b	8.50	8.50
32	37a	12.00	12.00
	37b	20.00	20.00
	38	20.00	20.00
	39	6.50	6.50
	40	5.50	6.50
33	41a	4.00	4.00
	41b	8.50	8.50
	42	30.00	30.00
	43	9.00	9.00
	44	3.75	3.75
34	45	18.50	18.50
	46	110.00	110.00
	47	65.00	65.00
	48	3.50	4.00
35	49	25.00	25.00
	50a	6.00	6.00
	50b	8.50	8.50
	51	6.00	6.00
	52 1a	25.00	25.00
	52 1b	32.50	32.50
	52 2a	11.50	11.50
	52 2b	14.50	14.50
	52 3a	8.50	8.50
	52 3b	11.50	11.50
	52 3c	11.50	11.50
	52 4a	20.00	20.00
	52 4b	25.00	25.00
36	53 1a	30.00	30.00
	53 1b	30.00	35.00
	53 1c	35.00	37.00
	53 2a	11.00	11.00
	53 2b	13.50	13.50
	53 2c	16.50	16.50
	53 3a	11.00	11.00
	53 3b	12.00	12.00
	53 3c	14.50	14.50
	53 4a	20.00	20.00
	53 4b	35.00	35.00
	53 4c	40.00	40.00
	54a	20.00	25.00
	54b	25.00	25.00

Goss

Page	Model No.	1981 £	1982 £
	55	16.50	16.50
	56	20.00	20.00
37	57a	3.75	3.75
	57b	10.00	10.00
	58	40.00	40.00
	59	4.00	4.00
	60	8.50	8.50
38	61	250.00	250.00
	62	150.00	150.00
	63	250.00	250.00
	64	150.00	150.00
39	65	5.00	5.00
	66	4.50	4.50
	67	30.00	30.00
	68a	5.00	5.00
	68b	10.00	10.00
40	69	4.50	4.50
	70	27.50	27.50
	71a	3.50	3.50
	71b	10.50	10.50
	72	8.00	8.00
41	73	4.50	4.50
	74a	50.00	50.00
	74b	75.00	75.00
	75a	45.00	45.00
	75b	20.00	25.00
	75c	100.00	100.00
	76	30.00	30.00
42	77	5.00	5.00
	78	8.00	8.00
	79a	5.00	5.00
	79b	8.50	8.50
	80a	65.00	65.00
	80b	100.00	100.00
	80c	200.00	200.00
43	81a	5.00	5.00
	81b	9.50	9.50
	82	10.00	10.00
	83	10.00	10.00
	84a	3.75	3.75
	84b	14.50	14.50
44	85	11.00	11.00

Page	Model No.	1981 £	1982 £
	86	7.00	7.00
	87	9.00	9.00
	88	3.75	3.75
45	89a	4.00	4.00
	89b	10.00	10.00
	90	8.50	8.50
	91	5.00	5.00
	92 1a	37.50	37.50
	92 1b	47.50	47.50
	92 2	100.00	100.00
	92 3a	40.00	40.00
	92 3b	55.00	55.00
	92 3c	85.00	85.00
46	93	5.00	5.00
	94	5.00	5.00
	95	4.00	4.00
	96	55.00	75.00
47	97	20.00	25.00
	98	12.00	12.50
	99	12.00	14.50
	100	18.00	18.50
48	101	18.50	18.50
	102	12.00	12.00
	103	12.00	14.50
	104	18.50	18.50
49	105	40.00	40.00
	106	16.50	16.50
	107a	47.50	47.50
	107b	250.00	250.00
	108	8.50	8.50
50	109	5.00	5.00
	110	10.00	11.50
	111a	4.00	4.00
	111b	8.00	8.00
	112	5.00	5.00
51	113a	5.00	5.00
	113b	11.50	11.50
	114	10.00	10.00
	115	11.00	11.00
	116	7.50	7.50
52	117a	4.00	4.00
	117b	10.00	10.00

Page	Model No.	1981 £	1982 £
	118	9.50	9.50
	119	30.00	35.00
	120a	4.75	5.00
	120b	14.50	14.50
53	121	4.00	4.50
	122	4.00	4.00
	123	3.50	7.00
	124a	7.00	7.00
	124b	25.00	27.50
54	125	4.00	4.00
	126	12.00	12.00
	127	3.50	3.50
	128	4.50	4.50
55	129a	4.00	4.00
	129b	11.50	11.50
	130	6.50	6.50
	131	3.75	4.00
	132	12.00	14.50
56	133	35.00	35.00
	134	40.00	40.00
	135	6.50	7.50
	136	6.50	6.50
	136a*	500.00	500.00

*New model Haamogi Amaui, Tonga

Page	Model No.	1981 £	1982 £
57	137	55.00	55.00
	138	8.00	8.00
	139	4.00	4.00
	140	3.75	3.75
58	141	10.50	10.50
	142	60.00	60.00
	143a	14.50	14.50
	143b	22.50	22.50
	144	4.00	4.00
59	145	6.50	6.50
	146a	25.00	25.00
	146b	27.50	27.50
	146c	40.00	40.00
	147	6.00	6.00
	148	5.00	5.00
60	149	5.00	5.00
	150	4.75	5.00
	151	3.75	3.75

Page	Model No.	1981 £	1982 £
	152	4.00	4.00
61	153	5.50	8.50
	154	32.50	34.50
	155a	4.00	4.00
	155b	13.50	13.50
	156	4.50	5.50
62	157	13.50	13.50
	158a	3.75	3.75
	158b	7.50	7.50
	159a	6.00	6.00
	159b	35.00	35.00
	160	6.00	6.00
63	161a	5.00	5.00
	161b	15.00	15.00
	162a	5.50	5.50
	162b	22.50	22.50
	163a	5.00	5.00
	163b	20.00	20.00
	164	3.75	3.75
64	165	10.00	10.00
	166	4.00	4.00
	167a	3.75	3.75
	167b	13.50	13.50
	168	7.00	7.00
65	169	8.50	8.50
	170	5.50	5.50
	171a	5.00	5.00
	171b	5.00	5.00
	172	5.00	5.00
66	173	7.50	7.50
	174a	4.00	4.00
	174b	12.50	12.50
	175	60.00	60.00
	176	26.50	26.50
67	177	3.50	3.50
	178a	3.75	3.75
	178b	12.00	14.50
	179a	4.00	4.00
	179b	17.50	17.50
	179c	850.00	1,000.00
	180a	4.50	4.50
	180b	8.50	8.50

Goss

Page	Model No.	1981 £	1982 £
68	181	5.00	5.00
	182	9.50	9.50
	183	10.50	10.50
	184a	8.50	8.50
	184b	18.00	18.00
69	185	4.00	4.00
	186a	4.00	4.00
	186b	16.50	16.50
	187	8.50	8.50
	188	10.00	10.00
70	189	20.00	20.00
	190	500.00	500.00
	191a	5.50	5.50
	191b	10.50	10.50
	192	12.00	12.00
71	193	18.00	18.00
	194	11.50	11.50
	195	5.00	5.00
	196	30.00	30.00
72	197	10.00	12.50
	198	8.00	8.00
	199	5.00	5.00
	200	6.00	6.00
73	200a	37.50	37.50
	200b*	80.00	80.00

*New model Maple Leaf of Canada

Page	Model No.	1981 £	1982 £
	201	12.50	12.50
	202	8.50	8.50
74	203 1a	225.00	225.00
	203 1b	300.00	300.00
	203 2a	See)	See)
	203 2b	Note)	Note)
	203 3a	225.00	225.00
	203 3b	300.00	300.00
	204	30.00	30.00
	205	25.00	27.50
75	206	3.50	3.50
	207a	3.75	3.75
	207b	10.00	10.00
	208	10.00	10.00
	209	3.75	3.75
76	210	8.50	10.00
	211	16.50	16.50
	212	14.50	14.50

Page	Model No.	1981 £	1982 £
	213a	3.75	3.75
Note: Not now believed to exist			
	213b	5.00	5.00
	213c	10.00	10.00
77	214	4.00	4.00
	215	3.75	3.75
	216	18.50	18.50
	217	5.50	5.50
78	218	3.75	3.75
	219	3.75	3.75
	220a	4.00	4.50
	220b	10.50	10.50
	221	17.50	17.50
79	222	3.50	3.50
	223	28.50	28.50
	224	3.75	3.75
	225a	75.00	75.00
	225b	125.00	125.00
80	226	8.00	8.00
	227	9.00	9.00
	228	3.75	3.75
	229a	6.00	6.00
	229b	18.50	18.50
81	230	32.50	37.50
	231a	4.00	4.00
	231b	25.00	25.00
	232	75.00	75.00
	233	110.00	110.00
82	234a	27.50	27.50
	234b	27.50	27.50
	235	11.00	11.00
	236	12.50	12.50
	237	8.50	8.50
83	238	4.00	4.00
	239a	3.75	3.75
	239b	9.50	9.50
	240	3.50	3.50
	241	3.50	3.50
84	242	4.00	4.00
	243	30.00	30.00
	244	50.00	50.00
	245	9.00	9.00
85	246a	30.00	30.00

Goss

Page	Model No.	1981 £	1982 £
	246b	85.00	85.00
	247	6.00	6.00
	248	4.50	4.50
	249a	8.50	8.50
	249b	13.50	13.50
86	250a	4.00	4.00
	250b	13.50	13.50
	251	8.00	9.50
	252a	7.50	7.50
	252b	14.50	14.50
	253a	4.50	4.50
	253b	8.50	8.50
87	254	5.00	5.00
	255a	6.50	7.50
	255b	12.00	12.00
	255c	17.50	17.50
	256	20.00	20.00
	257	15.00	15.00
88	258	4.50	4.50
	259	200.00	200.00
	260a	3.75	3.75
	260b	12.50	12.50
	260c	12.50	12.50
	261	3.75	3.75
89	262	200.00	200.00
	263a	4.00	4.00
	263b	12.50	14.50
	264	7.00	7.00
	265	14.50	14.50
90	266	5.00	5.00
	267	3.75	3.75
	268a	3.75	3.75
	268b	9.00	9.00
	269a	8.50	8.50
	269b	9.50	9.50
91	270a	7.00	7.00
	270b	9.00	9.00
	271	12.00	12.00
	272	5.50	5.50
	273	3.75	3.75
92	274	5.50	5.50
	275	4.00	4.00
	276	12.50	12.50

Goss

Page	Model No.	1981 £	1982 £
	277	6.00	6.00
93	277a	100.00	100.00
94	278a	4.00	4.00
	278b	4.00	4.00
	279a	13.00	13.50
	279b	18.50	18.50
	280	3.75	3.75
	281	4.00	4.00
95	282	10.00	10.00
	283	15.00	15.00
	284a	5.00	5.00
	284b	6.50	6.50
	284c	17.50	17.50
	284d	25.00	25.00
	285	8.50	8.50
96	286	13.50	16.50
	287a	8.50	8.50
	287b	13.50	13.50
	287c	17.50	17.50
	288	8.00	8.00
	289	5.00	5.00
97	290a	4.50	4.50
	290b	10.00	10.00
	291	18.50	18.50
	292	18.50	18.50
	293	7.50	7.50
98	294a	120.00	75.00
	294b	125.00	100.00
	294c	225.00	225.00
	295a	16.50	16.50
	295b	5.50	5.00
	295c	10.00	10.00
	295d	22.50	22.50
	296	225.00	300.00
	297	10.50	10.50
99	298a	350.00	350.00
	298b	200.00	200.00
	299a	3.75	3.75
	299b	8.50	8.50
	300	50.00	50.00
	301	18.00	18.00
100	302a	5.00	5.00

Goss

Page	Model No.	1981 £	1982 £
	302b	10.00	10.00
	303	7.50	7.50
	304	4.00	4.00
	305	40.00	40.00
101	306a	4.00	4.00
	306b	12.50	12.50
	307a	3.75	3.75
	307b	12.00	12.00
	308	11.00	11.00
105	309	14.50	14.50
	310	35.00	35.00
106	311	17.50	19.50
	312	17.50	21.50
	313	14.50	14.50
109	314	18.50	18.50
	315	16.50	16.50
	316	14.50	14.50
	317	35.00	35.00
110	318	16.50	16.50
	319	90.00	90.00
	320	25.00	29.50
113	321	250.00	400.00
	322a	100.00	100.00
	322b	275.00	275.00
114	323a	50.00	50.00
	323b	275.00	275.00
	324a	120.00	120.00
	324b	300.00	300.00
	325	1,000.00	1,000.00
115	326	22.50	22.50
	326a*	125.00	125.00
	326b*	150.00	150.00

*New models — a. white unglazed, b. brown

Page	Model No.	1981 £	1982 £
	327a	40.00	40.00
	327b	38.00	38.00
	327c	150.00	150.00
	327d	200.00	200.00
	327e*	85.00	100.00
	327f*	35.00	35.00

*New models — e. lidded, white unglazed, f. dished, white glazed

Page	Model No.	1981 £	1982 £
	328	25.00	25.00
	329	20.00	20.00

Page	Model No.	1981 £	1982 £
116	330a	100.00	100.00
	330b	150.00	150.00
	330c	250.00	250.00
	331a	50.00	50.00
	331b	50.00	50.00
	331c	200.00	200.00
	332a	550.00	550.00
	332b	750.00	750.00

Colour Plate 3. Caption should read: Eddystone Lighthouse, N.336. White glazed with Hastings Coat of Arms on red and turquoise ground. Height 125mm.

Page	Model No.	1981 £	1982 £
119	333a	35.00	35.00
	333b	35.00	35.00
	334	325.00	375.00
120	335	22.00	22.50
	335a*	150.00	200.00

*New model — Dungeness lighthouse

Page	Model No.	1981 £	1982 £
	336	17.50	18.50
	337	26.50	26.50
121	338	40.00	40.00
	339a	37.50	37.50
	339b	60.00	60.00
	339c	75.00	110.00
	340	375.00	400.00
	341	35.00	35.00
125	342	200.00	200.00
	343	300.00	325.00
	344	350.00	350.00
	345	300.00	300.00
126	346	50.00	60.00
	347	350.00	350.00
	348	350.00	350.00
	349	350.00	350.00
	349a*	500.00	500.00
	349b*	600.00	600.00

New models — a. Kangaroo, b. Tiger

Page	Model No.	1981 £	1982 £
127	350	300.00	300.00
	351	125.00	125.00
	352a	75.00	75.00
	352b	300.00	300.00
	353	300.00	300.00
128	354	500.00	500.00

*Note. The jaguar is now known to be a tiger.

Page	Model No.	1981 £	1982 £
	355	300.00	375.00
	356	300.00	350.00
129	357	250.00	250.00
	358	150.00	150.00
133	359a	200.00	200.00
	359b	250.00	250.00
	360a	120.00	120.00
	360b	180.00	200.00
	360c*	1,200.00	1,500.00

*New model — Old Market Cross, Buxton. Grey

Page	Model No.	1981 £	1982 £
	361	550.00	550.00
134	362a	150.00	150.00
	362b	300.00	300.00
	362c*	150.00	150.00
	362d*	200.00	200.00

*New models — c. white unglazed 150mm, d. white glazed 216mm

Page	Model No.	1981 £	1982 £
	363a	150.00	150.00
	363b	200.00	200.00
	363c	300.00	300.00
	364	600.00	600.00
	365	75.00	75.00
135	366	450.00	450.00
	367a	30.00	30.00
	367b	300.00	300.00
	368a	75.00	75.00
	368b	100.00	100.00
	368c	100.00	100.00
	369a	75.00	75.00
	369b	75.00	75.00
	369c	125.00	125.00
136	370a	200.00	200.00
	370b	225.00	225.00
	370c	300.00	300.00
	370d	300.00	300.00
	371a)	175.00	175.00
	371b)	250.00	250.00
Also in white glazed or unglazed		150.00	150.00
	372	1,250.00	1,250.00
139	373a	125.00	125.00
	373b	250.00	175.00
	374a	32.50	30.00
	374b	52.50	55.00

Page	Model No.	1981 £	1982 £
	375	350.00	350.00
140	376	45.00	45.00
	377	45.00	45.00
141	378	1,000.00	1,000.000
	379	75.00	75.00
	380a	125.00	125.00
	380b	200.00	200.00
	381	500.00	500.00
142	382	10.00	10.00
	383	55.00	55.00
	384	400.00	400.00
145	385	25.00	25.00
	386a	40.00	35.00
	386b	55.00	40.00
146	387a	40.00	40.00
	387b	50.00	50.00
	388a	30.00	30.00
	388b	40.00	40.00
	389a	40.00	40.00
	389b	65.00	65.00
147	390	90.00	110.00
	391	50.00	50.00
	392	50.00	50.00
	393	70.00	70.00
148	394	150.00	150.00
	395	80.00	80.00
	396	75.00	95.00
	397	70.00	70.00
149	398	175.00	175.00
	399	150.00	150.00
	400	150.00	150.00
	401	225.00	225.00
150	402	350.00	350.00
	403	325.00	325.00
153	405	25.00	25.00
	406	32.50	32.50
154	408	225.00	225.00
	409	175.00	175.00
	410	30.00	30.00
	411	1,000.00	1,000.00
155	413	150.00	150.00

Page	Model No.	1981 £	1982 £
	413a*	350.00	350.00
*New model — Newcastle Castle, brown			
	416	75.00	75.00
	417	100.00	100.00
	419	75.00	75.00
159	420	600.00	600.00
	421a	65.00	65.00
	421b	85.00	85.00
	421c	140.00	140.00
	421d	200.00	200.00
	422a	125.00	125.00
	422b	200.00	225.00
	422c	300.00	300.00
	423	850.00	850.00
160	424a	80.00	80.00
	424b	70.00	70.00
	424c	150.00	150.00
	424d	130.00	140.00
	425	225.00	225.00
	426a	115.00	115.00
	426b	115.00	115.00
	427	400.00	400.00
161	428	750.00	750.00
	429 1a	85.00	85.00
	429 1b	75.00	75.00
	429 1c	75.00	75.00
	429 1d	70.00	70.00
	429 1e	225.00	225.00
	429 2	600.00	600.00
	430	145.00	145.00
	431a	185.00	195.00
	431b	175.00	175.00
162	432	1,500.00	1,500.00
	433	550.00	550.00
	434a	70.00	70.00
	434b	60.00	60.00
	434c	175.00	175.00
	434d	140.00	150.00
	435	350.00	350.00
163	436	1,500.00	1,500.00
	437	1,250.00	1,250.00
	438a	105.00	105.00

Page	Model No.	1981 £	1982 £
	438b	95.00	95.00
	439a	140.00	140.00
	439b	130.00	130.00
164	440	650.00	650.00
	441	325.00	350.00
	442	275.00	275.00
	443a	125.00	115.00
	443b	110.00	110.00
165	444 1a	150.00	150.00
	444 1b	140.00	140.00
	444 2	110.00	110.00
	445a	85.00	85.00
	445b	85.00	85.00
	446a	95.00	95.00
	446b	85.00	85.00
	446c	165.00	165.00
	446d	145.00	145.00
	447a	80.00	80.00
	447b	250.00	250.00
166	448a	50.00	50.00
	448b	100.00	100.00
	448c	175.00	175.00
	449	285.00	285.00
	450a	130.00	130.00
	450b	120.00	120.00
	451	375.00	375.00
167	452	350.00	350.00
	453	1,000.00	1,000.00
	454a	90.00	90.00
	454b	225.00	225.00
	454c	250.00	250.00
	455	400.00	400.00
168	456a	145.00	130.00
	456b	130.00	130.00
	457	200.00	200.00
	458 1a	70.00	70.00
	458 1b	60.00	60.00
	458 1c	175.00	175.00
	458 1d	160.00	160.00
	458 2	80.00	80.00
	458 3	105.00	105.00
169	459	1,000.00	1,000.00

Page	Model No.	1981 £	1982 £
	460a	100.00	100.00
	460b	250.00	250.00
	461a	125.00	120.00
	461b	85.00	110.00
	461c	225.00	225.00
	462a	325.00	325.00
	462b	325.00	325.00
170	463	285.00	285.00
	464a	725.00	725.00
	464b	775.00	775.00
	465	225.00	225.00
173	466	75.00	100.00
	467a	75.00	100.00
	467b	100.00	100.00
	467c	200.00	250.00
	468	6.00	6.00
174	469a	50.00	50.00
	469b	75.00	75.00
	470a	7.50	8.50
	470b	8.50	18.50
175	471	50.00	50.00
	472	10.00	10.00
	473	6.50	9.50
	474a	75.00	75.00
	474b	25.00	30.00
	474c	30.00	30.00
	474d	45.00	45.00
	474e	30.00	30.00
	474f	40.00	40.00
	474g	50.00	50.00
176	475a	6.50	6.50
	475b	5.50	6.50
	475c	7.50	7.50
	475d	9.50	9.50
	475e	10.50	10.50
	475f	12.00	14.50
	475g	35.00	35.00
	475h	55.00	85.00
	476	75.00	87.50
	477	10.00	12.00
	478a	5.50	6.50
	478b	8.50	8.50

Page	Model No.	1981 £	1982 £
	478c	12.50	12.50
177	479a	45.00	45.00
	479b	75.00	75.00
	480	1,000.00	1,250.00
	481	1,000.00	1,250.00
178	482	10.00	12.00
	483a	32.50	32.50
	483b	95.00	95.00
	483c	145.00	125.00
	484	300.00	300.00
179	485	200.00	200.00
	485a*	200.00	200.00
	485b*	200.00	200.00
	486	100.00	100.00

*New models — a. Cliftonville vase, 70mm. b. Cliftonville jug, 180mm.

*With any arms